Gus the Christmas Star

by Frank Remkiewicz

For David and Jean—Cheers!

Copyright © 2012 by Frank Remkiewicz

All rights reserved. Published by Scholastic Inc.
SCHOLASTIC, and associated logos are
trademarks and/or registered trademarks of Scholastic Inc.
Lexile is a registered trademark of MetaMetrics, Inc.

ISBN 978-0-545-46910-4

12 11 10 9 8 7 6 5 4   14 15 16 17/0

Printed in the U.S.A.   40
First printing, November 2012

Gus the Christmas Star

Gus goes to school.

Today is the class play.

But first they trim the tree.

Then they give gifts.

Soon it is show time.

The class gets dressed.

No more hats!

What is that?

Now Gus has a hat.

He has bells, too.

Gus will ring the bells.

Moms and dads are here.

They will watch the play.

Now the class will sing.

Jingle bells, jingle bells . . .

Where is Gus?

There he is!

Where are the bells?

There they are!

Good show, Gus!